P I A N O   S T U D I E S   A L B U M

3 & 4

CENTENNIAL

ROYAL CONSERVATORY

18 86

OF MUSIC · TORONTO

Celebration
SERIES

ISBN 0-88797-295-0

FREDERICK
HARRIS
MUSIC

Official Examination Studies of the
Royal Conservatory of Music – Grades 3 & 4

Études officielles des examens du
Royal Conservatory of Music – Niveaux 3 & 4

The Centennial Celebration Series of the Royal Conservatory of Music offers teachers, students, and those who play the piano solely for their own enjoyment, a carefully selected and well-balanced collection of compositions of the highest quality. Pianists at all levels of development will find the series to be of exceptional musical and pedagogical value.

This series is the collective product of more than 100 years of teaching and performing experience, and represents countless hours of dedicated effort by compilers and editors from the staff of the Royal Conservatory of Music and The Frederick Harris Music Co., Limited. The repertoire and studies in this series are drawn from official Royal Conservatory of Music examination material as determined by the Royal Conservatory of Music Piano Syllabus. Students and teachers are urged to consult the most recent Syllabus for current examination requirements and procedures.

Editorial markings have been applied conservatively for the convenience of the performer. Students and teachers are encouraged to consider interpretive alternatives in the interest of individually sensitive and imaginative performances. With the exception of *da capo* indications, repeats should be omitted during examinations.

The Royal Conservatory of Music takes pride in its 100 years of service to the international music community and wishes all who use the Centennial Celebration Series the joy of discovery and much musical satisfaction.

La Centennial Celebration Series du Royal Conservatory of Music offre aux professeurs, aux étudiants, et à ceux qui jouent du piano pour leur seul plaisir, une collection de la plus haute qualité, choisie avec soin et bien équilibrée. Pianistes de tout calibre trouveront cette série d'une grande valeur tout autant musicale que pédagogique.

Cette série, la réalisation conjuguée de plus de 100 ans d'expérience collective dans l'enseignement et l'interprétation de la musique, représente des heures incalculables de travail de la part des compilateurs et des éditeurs, membres du personnel du Royal Conservatory of Music et de la Frederick Harris Music Co., Limited. Le répertoire et les études font partie du programme officiel décrit dans le syllabus pour piano du Royal Conservatory of Music. Etudiants et professeurs sont priés de consulter le syllabus le plus récent pour les exigences et les règlements des examens.

Les ajouts d'édition dans ce livre ont été appliqués avec soin pour faciliter l'interprétation de l'exécutant. Dans l'intérêt de la sensibilité individuelle et de l'exécution imaginative, étudiants et professeurs considéreront différents choix d'interprétation. A l'exception des indications *da capo*, les reprises devraient être omises aux examens.

Le Royal Conservatory of Music est très fier de ses 100 années au service de la communauté musicale internationale. Le Conservatoire souhaite à tous les usagers de la Centennial Celebration Series une grande satisfaction musicale et la joie de la découverte.

Royal Conservatory of Music
273 Bloor Street West, Toronto, Ontario, M5S 1W2

Piano Studies Album 3 & 4

TABLE OF CONTENTS

GRADE 3

Study No. 1	4	*Gurlitt, C.*	4	Étude n° 1
Study No. 2	5	*Czerny, C.*	5	Étude n° 2
Study No. 3	6	*Schytte, L.*	6	Étude n° 3
Study No. 4	7	*Bertini, H.*	7	Étude n° 4
Study No. 5, Op. 139, No. 7	8	*Czerny, C.*	8	Étude n° 5, op. 139, n° 7
Study No. 6, Op. 37, No. 17	9	*Lemoine, A.H.*	9	Étude n° 6, op. 37, n° 17
Study No. 7	10	*Schytte, L.*	10	Étude n° 7
Study No. 8	11	*Hummel, J.N.*	11	Étude n° 8
Study No. 9	12	*Gurlitt, C.*	12	Étude n° 9
Study No. 10, Op. 32, No. 12	13	*Gedike, A.*	13	Étude n° 10, op. 32, n° 12
Study No. 11, Op. 139, No. 24	14	*Czerny, C.*	14	Étude n° 11, op. 139, n° 24
Study No. 12, Op. 100, No. 2	15	*Burgmüller, J.F.*	15	Étude n° 12, op. 100, n° 2
("L'Arabesque")				("L'Arabesque")
Study No. 13, Op. 169, No. 11	16	*Biehl, A.*	16	Étude n° 13, op. 169, n° 11
Study No. 14, Op. 43, No. 1	17	*Miaskovsky, N.*	17	Étude n° 14, op. 43, n° 1
Study No. 15	18	*Berens, H.*	18	Étude n° 15
Study No. 16	19	*Vitlin, V.*	19	Étude n° 16

GRADE 4

Study No. 1	20	*Maykapar, S.*	20	Étude n° 1
Study No. 2, Op. 599, No. 85	21	*Czerny, C.*	21	Étude n° 2, op. 599, n° 85
Study No. 3, Op. 36, No. 26	22	*Gedike, A.*	22	Étude n° 3, op. 36, n° 26
Study No. 4, Op. 141, No. 4	23	*Gurlitt, C.*	23	Étude n° 4, op. 141, n° 4
Study No. 5, Op. 70, No. 50	24	*Berens, H.*	24	Étude n° 5, op. 70, n° 50
Study No. 6, Op. 176, No. 24	25	*Duvernoy, J.-B.*	25	Étude n° 6, op. 176, n° 24
Study No. 7, Op. 100, No. 11	26	*Burgmüller, J.F.*	26	Étude n° 7, op. 100, n° 11
Study No. 8, Op. 599, No. 83	27	*Czerny, C.*	27	Étude n° 8, op. 599, n° 83
Study No. 9	28	*Golubovskaya, N.*	28	Étude n° 9
Study No. 10	29	*Klin, V.*	29	Étude n° 10
Study No. 11	30	*Czerny, C.*	30	Étude n° 11
Study No. 12, Op. 100, No. 18	31	*Burgmüller, J.F.*	31	Étude n° 12, op. 100, n° 18
Study No. 13, Op. 45, No. 2	32	*Heller, S.*	32	Étude n° 13, op. 45, n° 2
Study No. 14	34	*Gnessina, E.*	34	Étude n° 14
Study No. 15, Op. 599, No. 45	35	*Czerny, C.*	35	Étude n° 15, op. 599, n° 45
Study No. 16, Op. 65, No. 42	36	*Loeschhorn, A.*	36	Étude n° 16, op. 65, n° 42

STUDY NO. 1 / ETUDE Nº 1

GRADE 3

Cornelius Gurlitt
(1820-1901)

Moderato (M.M. ♩ = 72-76)

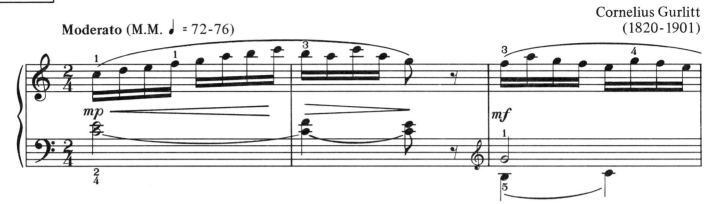

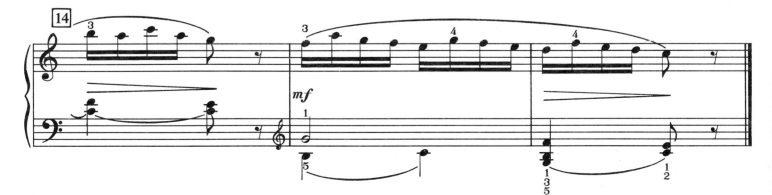

STUDY NO. 2 / ETUDE Nº 2

GRADE 3

Carl Czerny
(1791-1857)

Allegretto (M.M. ♩ = 112-126)

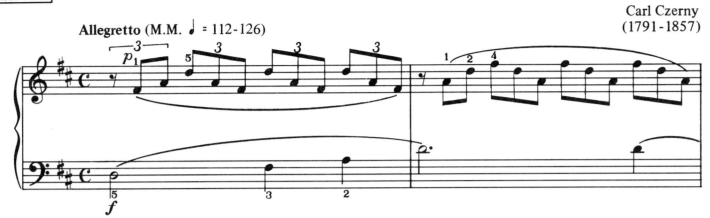

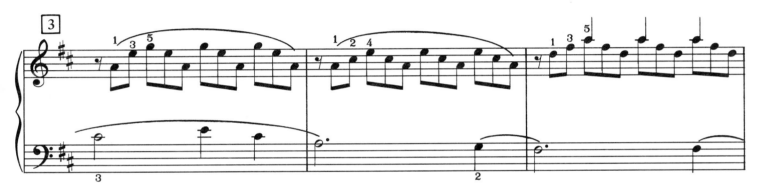

STUDY NO. 3 / ETUDE Nº 3

GRADE 3

Ludwig Schytte
(1848-1909)

Allegro moderato (M.M. ♩ = 84-92)

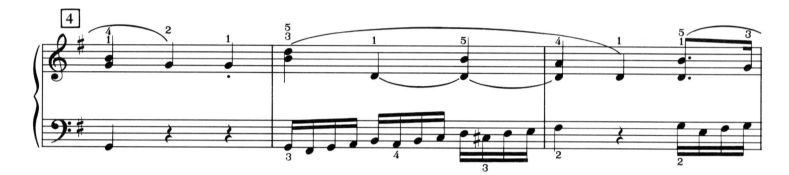

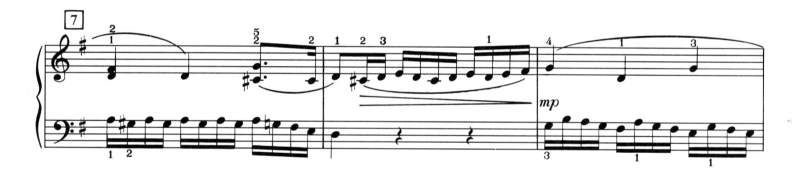

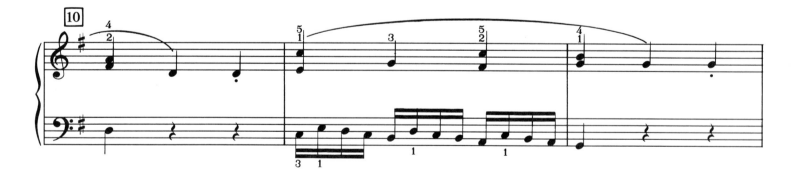

STUDY NO. 4 / ETUDE No 4

GRADE 3

Henri Bertini
(1798-1876)

Allegretto (M.M. ♩ = 152-160)

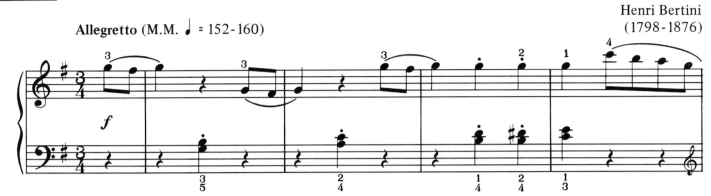

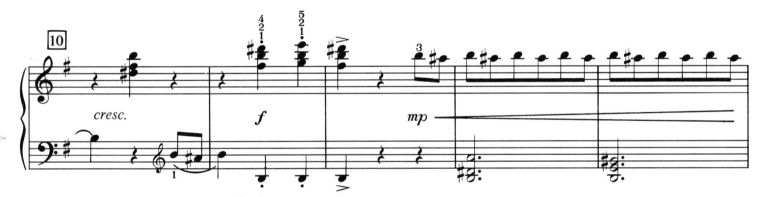

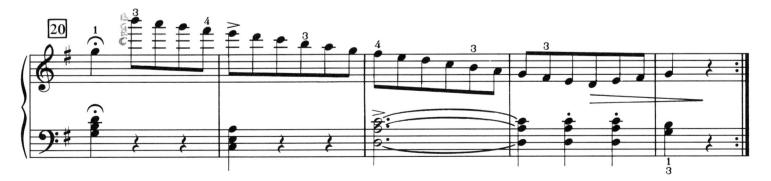

STUDY NO. 5 / ETUDE Nº 5
Op. 139, No. 7

GRADE 3

Carl Czerny
(1791-1857)

Allegretto (M.M. ♩. = 69-80)

STUDY NO. 6 / ETUDE Nº 6
Op. 37, No. 17*

GRADE 3

Antoine Henry Lemoine
(1786-1854)

Allegretto (M.M. ♩ = 84-92)

*Abridged/Abrégé

STUDY NO. 7 / ETUDE No 7

after/après Ludwig Schytte
(1848-1909)

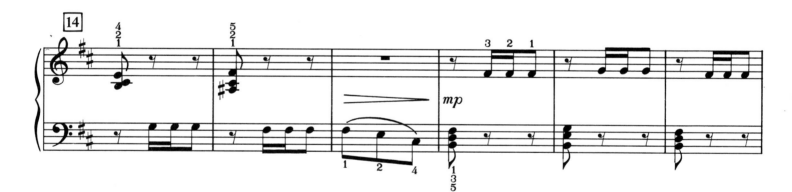

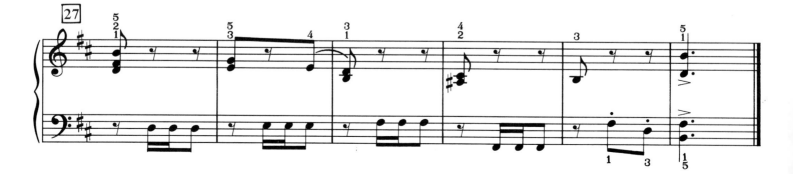

STUDY NO. 8 / ETUDE Nº 8

GRADE 3

Johann Nepomuk Hummel
(1778-1837)

Andante con moto (M.M. ♩ = 96-108)

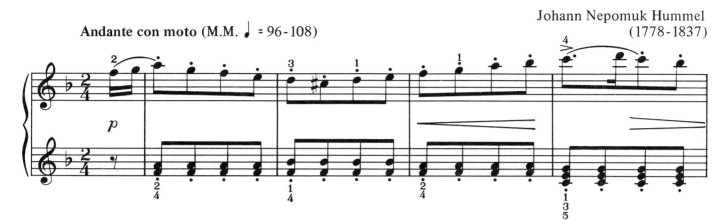

STUDY NO. 9 / ETUDE No 9

GRADE 3

Cornelius Gurlitt
(1820-1901)

Allegretto (M.M. ♩. = 54-60)

STUDY NO. 10 / ETUDE № 10
Op. 32, No. 12

GRADE 3

Moderato quasi andantino (M.M. ♩ = 80-84)

Alexander Gedike
(1877-1957)

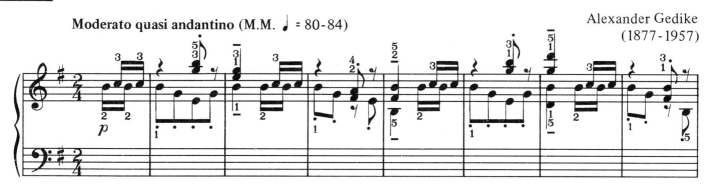

STUDY NO. 11 / ETUDE Nº 11
Op. 139, No. 24

GRADE 3

Carl Czerny
(1791-1857)

Allegro (M.M. ♪ = 160-168)

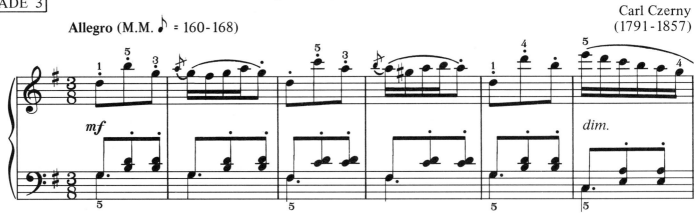

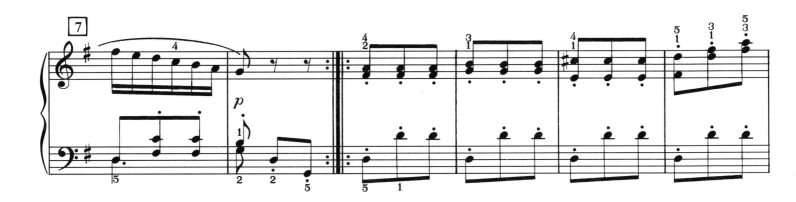

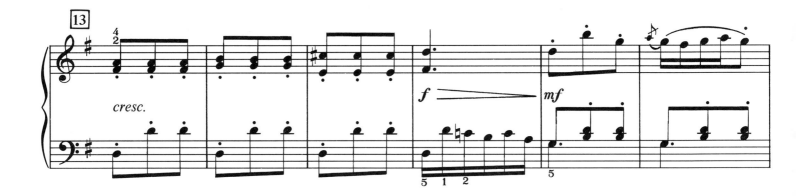

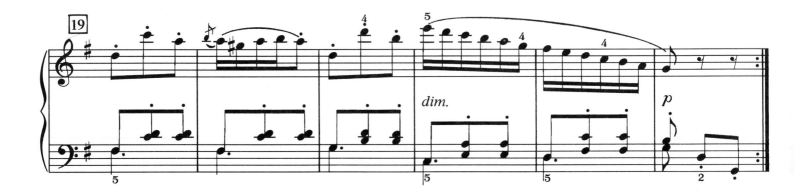

STUDY NO. 12 / ETUDE № 12
Op. 100, No. 2 ("L'Arabesque")

Johann Friedrich Burgmüller
(1806-1874)

Allegro scherzando (M.M. ♩ = 104-116)

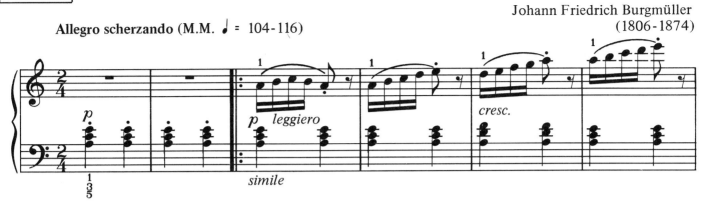

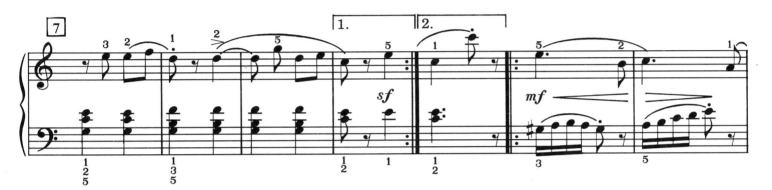

STUDY NO. 13 / ETUDE Nº 13
Op. 169, No. 11

GRADE 3

Albert Biehl
(1833-c. 1892)

Vivace (M.M. ♩ = 144-152)

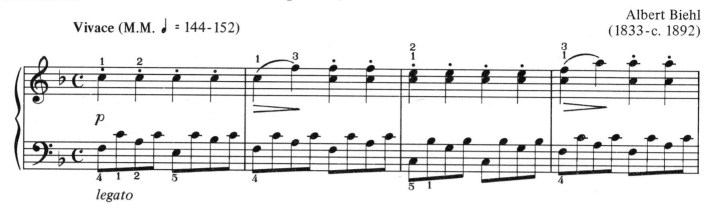

legato

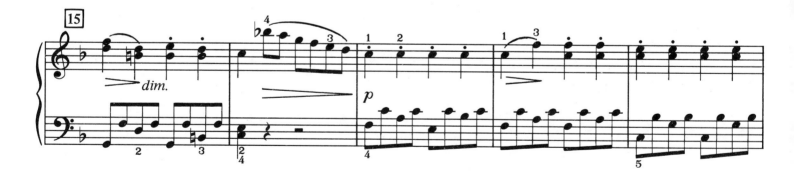

STUDY NO. 14 / ETUDE № 14
Op. 43, No. 1

Nicolas Miaskovsky
(1881-1950)

GRADE 3

Allegro giocoso (M.M. ♩ = 76-80)

f legato

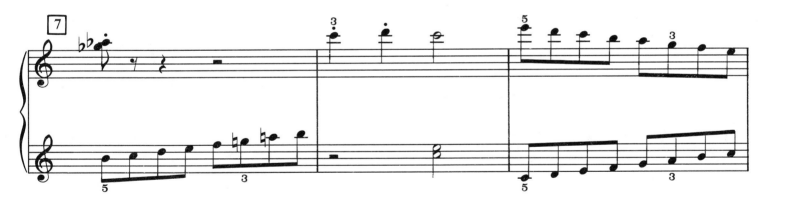

STUDY NO. 15 / ETUDE № 15

GRADE 3

Allegro (M.M. ♩ = 84-96)

Hermann Berens
(1826-1880)

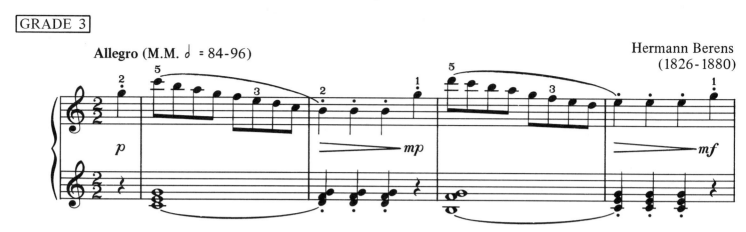

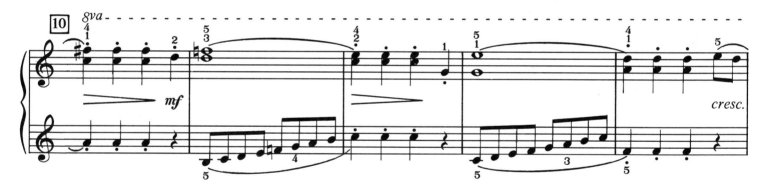

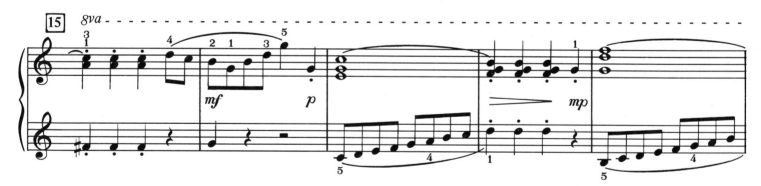

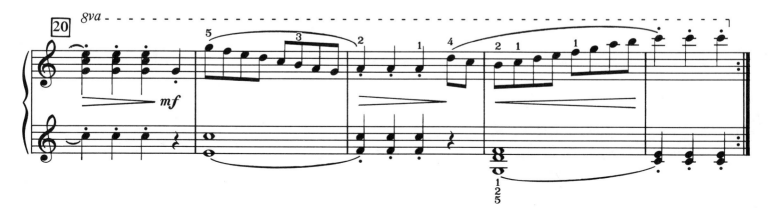

STUDY NO. 16 / ETUDE № 16

Moderato (M.M. ♩ = 126-132)

V. Vitlin

STUDY NO. 1 / ETUDE No 1

GRADE 4

Samuel Maykapar
(1867-1938)

Allegro (M.M. ♩ = 104-108)

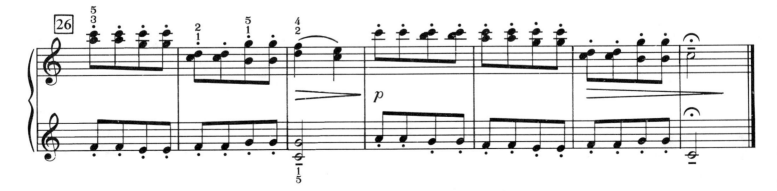

STUDY NO. 2 / ETUDE № 2
Op. 599, No. 85*

GRADE 4

Carl Czerny
(1791-1857)

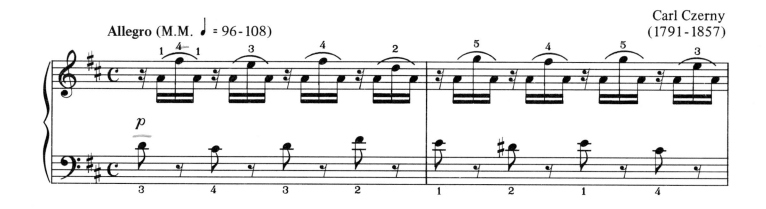

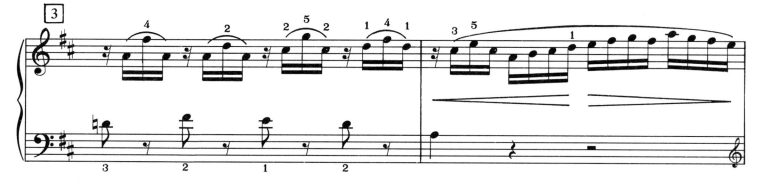

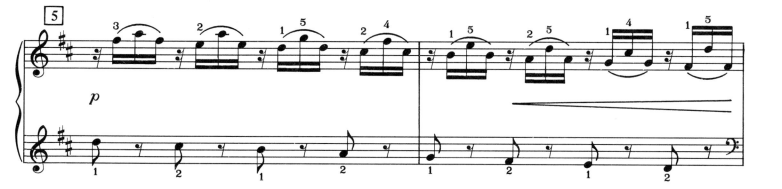

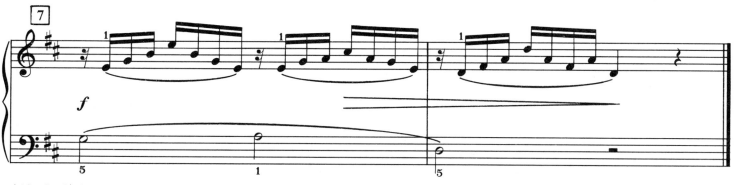

*Abridged/Abrégé

STUDY NO. 3 / ETUDE Nº 3
Op. 36, No. 26

GRADE 4

Alexander Gedike
(1877-1957)

Allegro marciale (M.M. ♩ = 84-96)

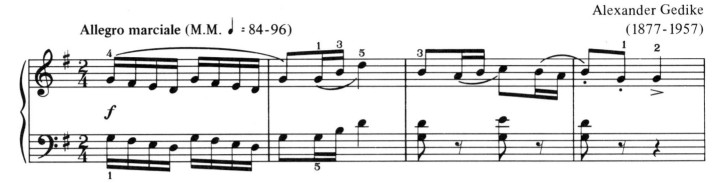

STUDY NO. 4 / ETUDE Nº 4
Op. 141, No. 4

GRADE 4

Cornelius Gurlitt
(1820-1901)

Allegro (M.M. ♩ = 88-96)

STUDY NO. 5 / ETUDE No 5
Op. 70, No. 50

GRADE 4

Hermann Berens
(1826-1880)

Allegro (M.M. ♩ = 84-100)

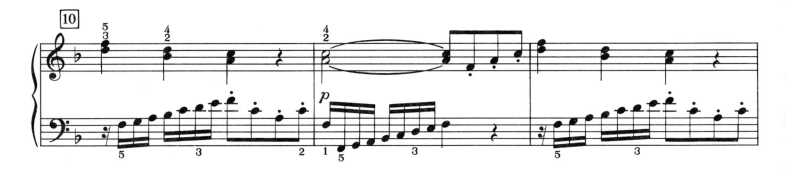

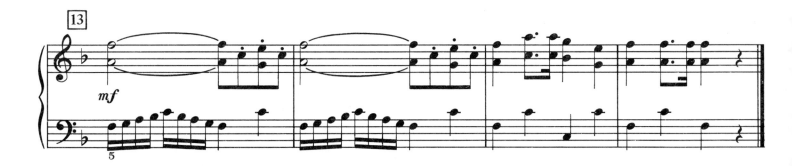

STUDY NO. 6 / ETUDE Nº 6
Op. 176, No. 24

GRADE 4

Jean-Baptiste Duvernoy
(1802-1880)

Allegretto (M.M. ♩ = 100-104)

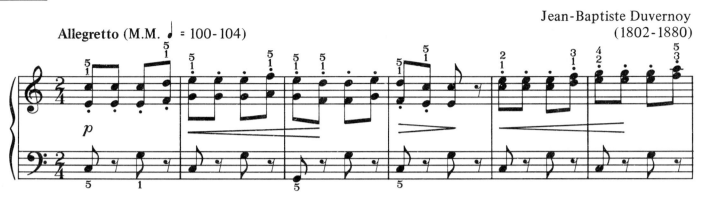

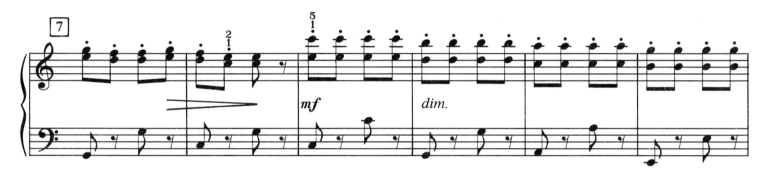

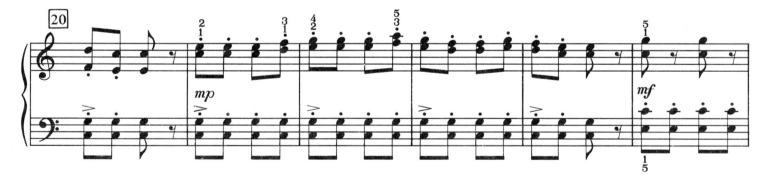

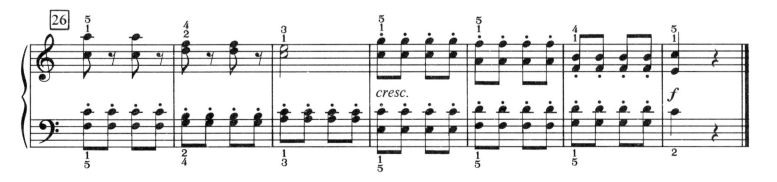

STUDY NO. 7 / ETUDE Nº 7
Op. 100, No. 11

GRADE 4

Johann Friedrich Burgmüller
(1806-1874)

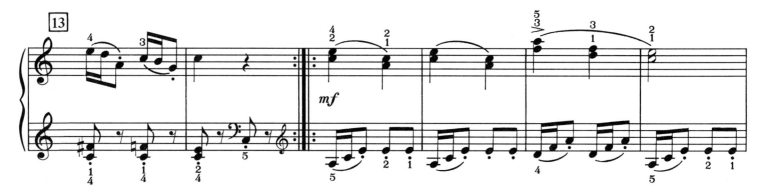

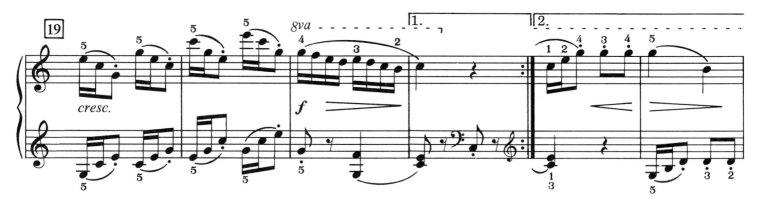

STUDY NO. 8 / ETUDE № 8
Op. 599, No. 83

GRADE 4

Carl Czerny
(1791-1857)

Allegro (M.M. ♩. = 60-66)

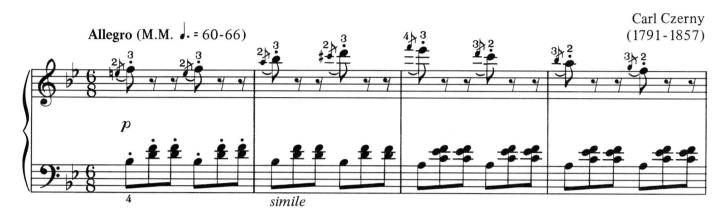

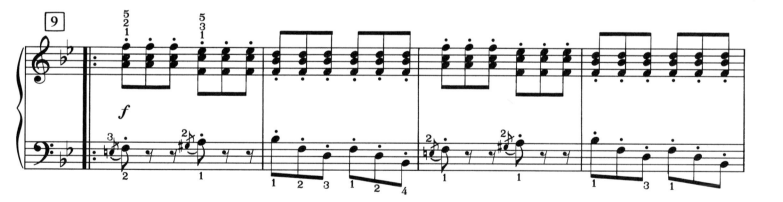

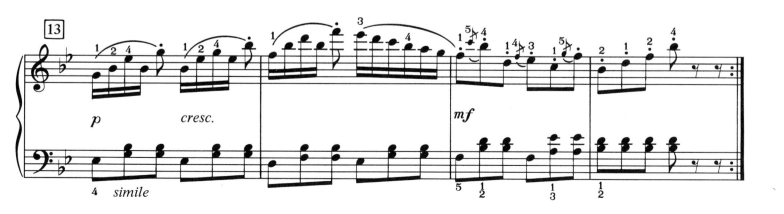

STUDY NO. 9 / ETUDE No 9

GRADE 4

Nadezhda Golubovskaya
(1891-1975)

STUDY NO. 10 / ETUDE No 10

GRADE 4

V. Klin

Allegro non troppo (M.M. ♩ = 104-112)

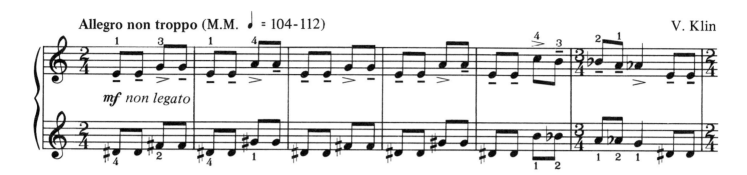

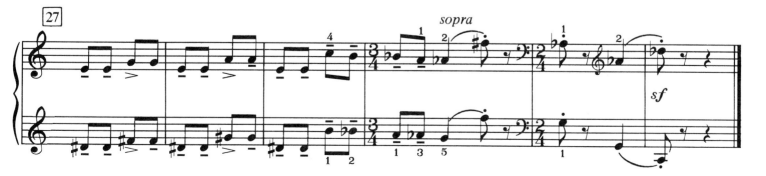

STUDY NO. 11 / ETUDE Nº 11

GRADE 4

Carl Czerny
(1791-1857)

Allegretto (M.M. ♩ = 96-104)

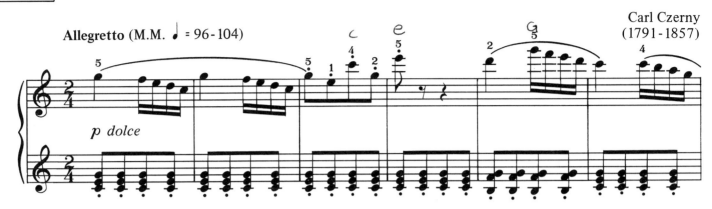

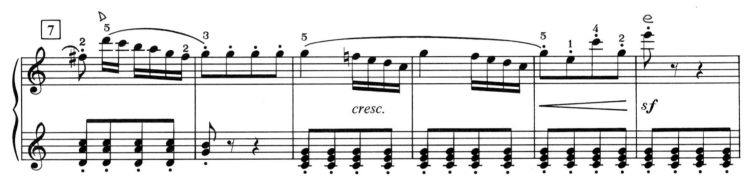

STUDY NO. 12 / ETUDE № 12
Op. 100, No. 18

GRADE 4

Johann Friedrich Burgmüller
(1806-1874)

Allegro agitato (M.M. ♩ = 88-96)

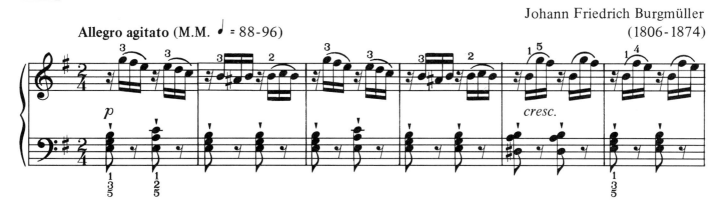

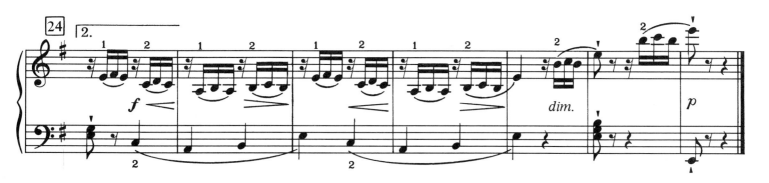

STUDY NO. 13 / ETUDE Nº 13
Op. 45, No. 2

Stephen Heller
(1814-1888)

Allegro vivace (M.M. ♩ = 112-116)

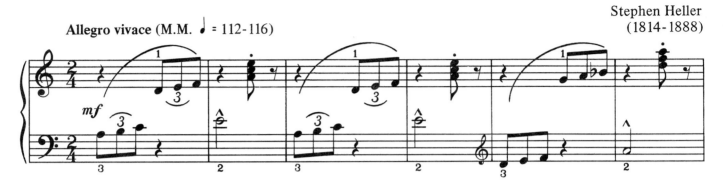

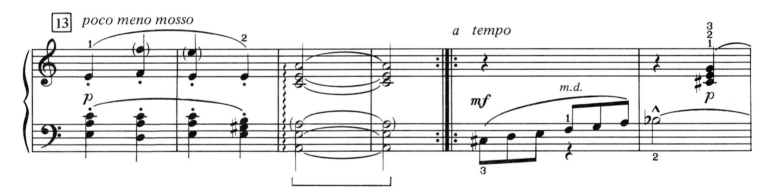

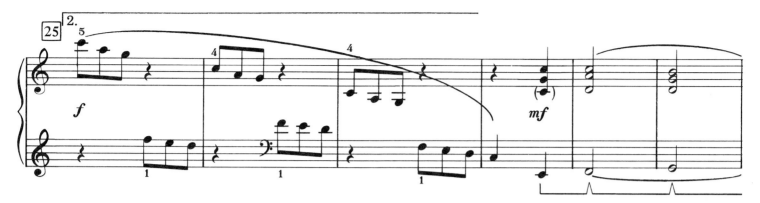

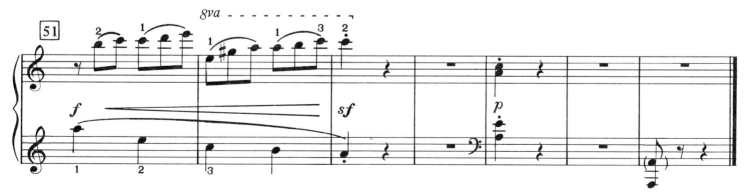

STUDY NO. 14 / ETUDE № 14

GRADE 4

Elena Gnessina
(1874-1967)

Allegretto grazioso (M.M. ♩ = 69-72)

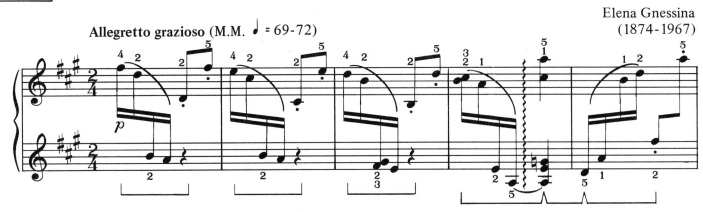

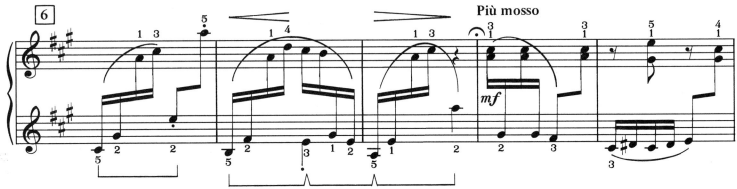

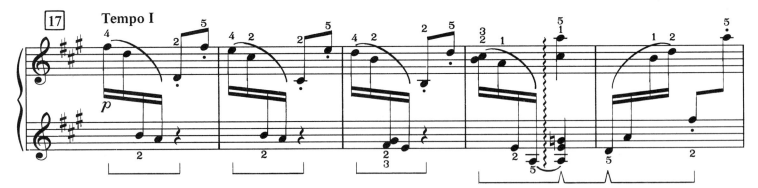

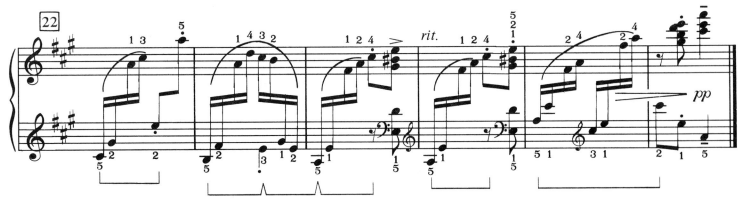

STUDY NO. 15 / ETUDE № 15
Op. 599, No. 45

GRADE 4

Carl Czerny
(1791-1857)

Allegretto (M.M. ♩ = 84-88)

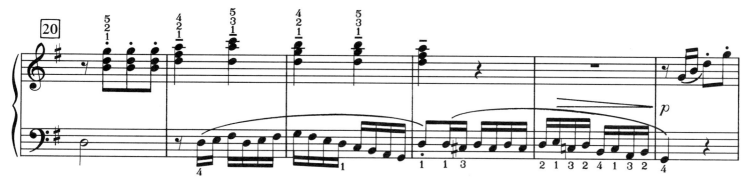

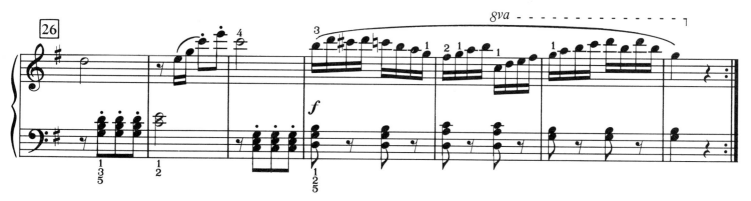

STUDY NO. 16 / ETUDE Nº 16
Op. 65, No. 42

Albert Loeschhorn
(1819 -1905)

GRADE 4

Andantino (M.M. ♩ = 84-88)

con pedale

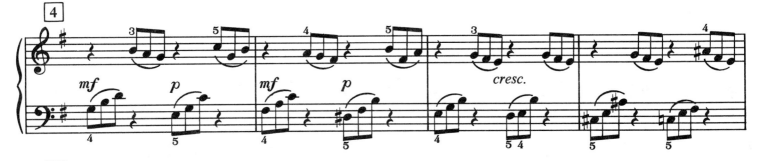